This book belongs to:

Published 2013. Century Books Ltd.
Unit 1, Upside Station Building Solsbro Road,
Torquay, Devon, UK, TQ26FD

books@centurybooksltd.co.uk

centum

Contents

Meet
1D

Hiya everyone!

Wow, we've been one busy band and it has been a blast. Not only have we had a number-one single and won a BRIT Award, but we have also been travelling the world on our 'Take Me Home' Tour, playing sold-out gigs and released our 3D movie – This Is Us.

Our fans are truly amazing – we owe all our success to you. We just want to say a massive thank you for always being there for us. So we've created this book packed with a ton of facts, our story so far, games, puzzles and activities, loads of pics and more! So grab a pen and enjoy . . .

The boys doing what they do best – looking super-hot at NRJ Music Awards 2013.

ONE DIRECTION

Mini-Me! The guys check out their official 1D dolls in California.

9

Harry

'Come on out and dance, if you get the chance.'

Tweet by Harry

The Basics:

Full Name: Harry Edward Styles

DOB: 1st February 1994

Home Town: Holmes Chapel, Cheshire

Star Sign: Aquarius

Height: 5'10

Family Tree:

Mum: Anne
Dad: Des
Sister: Gemma

Interesting Ink:

Harry's tattoos include
a ship and a heart

Top Tweet:

'Soooo... I went to download our
album this morning. And my
card got declined. Hahaha!'

Random Fact:

Harry 'Curls' Styles
had straight hair
when he was little!

I ♥ HARRY

Harry Mini-Quiz

1. For Harry's *X Factor* audition he sang, 'Isn't She ....,'
- a. Beautiful
- b. Lovely
- c. Ugly

2. What is Harry's middle name?
- a. Boris
- b. George
- c. Edward

3. What is Harry's mum's name?
- a. Mary
- b. Jolene
- c. Anne

Are you an expert on all things Harry? Time to show off...

Check answers on page 154

4. Harry comes from this county.
a. Cheshire
b. Cumbria
c. Cornwall

5. What is Harry's star sign?
a. Virgo
b. Aquarius
c. Capricorn

HARRY

Harry

ONE DIRECTION

I ♥ HARRY

Liam

'Hi everyone just wanted to say...
I just had a moment... Can't believe
what's actually happened or how
I got here...'

Tweet by Liam

The Basics:

Full Name: Liam
James Payne

DOB: 29th August
1993

Home Town:
Wolverhampton

Star Sign: Virgo

Height: 5'10

Family Tree:

Mum: Karen
Dad: Geoff
Sisters: Ruth
and Nicola

Interesting Ink:

Liam has a set of
chevrons on his arm.

Top Tweet.

'Ohh I wish I could follow all of you
at once but Twitter wont let me, be
back to follow more soonnnn! :)'

Random Fact.

Lovely Liam plans to
name his firstborn child
Taylor whether it is a
boy or a girl!

I ♥ LIAM

Liam Wordsearch

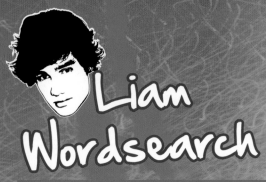

There are twelve words hidden below. Can you find them? They may be written forwards, backwards, up, down or diagonally.

B	A	E	S	R	E	N	O	I	T	C	E	R	I	D
X	V	O	N	E	S	C	I	M	R	I	K	P	O	S
F	A	J	I	T	R	U	F	A	M	E	S	U	T	N
A	L	A	R	T	E	D	S	L	G	N	R	S	X	O
C	W	M	P	I	Q	K	H	U	O	A	L	U	S	T
T	I	E	T	W	O	U	Y	R	R	J	I	S	T	P
O	X	S	I	T	E	P	V	M	A	N	A	S	A	M
R	E	I	C	Y	U	E	S	V	A	P	M	Y	H	A
Z	U	G	G	E	H	W	R	O	F	O	N	R	A	H
P	E	O	H	C	O	N	T	O	J	E	R	M	I	R
W	O	L	T	E	O	P	E	Q	U	I	K	C	A	E
Y	F	A	R	L	T	U	W	B	I	J	U	Y	E	V
H	I	A	E	S	T	D	O	G	R	I	V	X	T	L
O	Y	L	I	T	A	T	C	E	B	A	G	N	L	O
U	K	C	R	E	T	R	H	P	O	W	F	R	S	W

Check answers on page 154

1. WOLVERHAMPTON

2. PAYNE

3. FAME

4. X FACTOR

5. CHEVRONS

6. TWITTER

7. VIRGO

8. JAMES

9. TOUR

10. TATTOO

11. DIRECTIONERS

12. LIAM

LIAM

ONE DIRECTION

I ♥ LIAM

1D

Louis

'1000 days of being in the band? Wow that really is incredible :) Amazing that you guys have shaped our career! Thank you so much x.' Tweet by Louis

The Basics:

Full Name: Louis William Tomlinson

DOB: 24th December 1991

Home Town: Doncaster

Star Sign: Capricorn

Height: 5'9

Family Tree:

Mum: Johannah

Dad: Troy

Sisters: Georgia, Charlotte, Félicité and twins Daisy and Phoebe

Interesting Ink:

Louis has a compass on his arm.

Top Tweet.

'Wouldn't mind a good heart to heart with @zaynmalik right now! Missing you man!'

Random Fact.

Louis spent his first ever pay-check on adopting a chimpanzee called Larry!

I ♥ LOUIS

Louis
Spot the
Difference

We know you don't
need an excuse to
stare at luscious
Louis. Look closely
and you'll find
these two pics
don't match.

BBC RADIO 1'S
TEEN AWARD
BBC RADIO 1
2012
Best British Single
One Thing · One Direction

LOUIS

Can you
find all ten
differences?

ONE
DIRECTION

I ♥ LOUIS

1D

20

Check answers on page 154

Niall

'3 years since I first auditioned on X Factor! Wow! Time flies! Best 3 years of my life! All thanks to the best fans in the world! We love you' *Tweet by Niall*

The Basics:

Full Name: Niall James Horan

DOB: 13th September 1993

Home Town: Mullingar, Ireland

Star Sign: Virgo

Height: 5'7

Family Tree:

Mum: Maura
Dad: Bobby
Brother: Greg

Interesting Ink:

So far Niall is keeping quiet about whether he has joined the tattoo club. He claims that he tried to have 'Made in Ireland' tattooed on his bum but was told it was too squidgy. Aww!

Top Tweet:

'Just having one of those moments again.... so thankful to you guys for gettin us here. We are touring the world this year. It's just all so crazy.'

Random Fact:

When the boys were trying to decide what to call their band, Niall suggested 'Niall and the Potatoes!'

I ♥ NIALL

Niall Crossword

Check answers on page 154

Just how well
do you know
our Niall?
Time to test
yourself...

Across

3.   Niall's favourite colour.

6.   Niall comes from this Irish town.

Down

1.   .... Bublé is Niall's man-crush.

2.   Niall plays this instrument.

4.   His middle name.

5.   Niall's star sign.

Zayn

'So happy to be going home missed every1 so much! :) especially you ;) x x x x'
Tweet by Zayn

The Basics:

Full Name: Zayn Javadd Malik

DOB: 12th January 1993

Home Town: Bradford

Star Sign: Capricorn

Height: 5'9

Family Tree:

Mum: Tricia
Dad: Yasser
Sisters: Doniya,
Waliyha, Safaa

Interesting Ink:

The half-sleeve on Zayn's right forearm includes the word 'zap,' a microphone and a skull.

Top Tweet:

'Hi everyone, just a quick message to say I love all you guys, without your support I don't know what I'd do :) x'

Random Fact:

Before going on stage, Zayn has to brush his teeth! It has become a pre-gig ritual which he admits 'is a little bit weird.'

I ♥ ZAYN

Zayn Maze

Zayn has been posing for a super-stylish photo shoot and he is running late. The 1D boys are all waiting on the red carpet for the opening of This is Us in London... But where is Zayn?

Start

Can you save the day and steer his taxi straight to the cinema?

ZAYN

ONE DIRECTION

I ZAYN

1D

Finish

?

Check answer on page 154

Performing an intimate gig in California. Wish we were there!

Back to School!

31

Me...

I ♥ HARRY
LIAM
LOUIS
NIAII
ZAYN

Name: _____

Age: _____

Birthday: _____

Star Sign: _____

Address: _____

_____

School: _____

Email: _____

Twitter profile: _____

Hair Colour: _____

Eye Colour: _____

Height: _____

Signature: _____

BFF: _____

Pets: _____

_____

I ♥ 1D

My favourite **1D** song:

_____
_____
_____

My favourite **1D** lyric:

_____
_____
_____

My family tree:

My favourite pic of me:

This picture was taken:

Blast From the Past

Take a peek at these pictures of the boys. How much has changed!

Use the spaces to write down what you thought about the boys, then and now.

Wow! Such a lot has happened to Harry, Liam, Louis, Niall and Zayn in just a few years. They started out dreaming of stardom in different parts of the UK. Now they're best of friends and conquering the world.

When I first saw One Direction:

I thought...

I loved _____ the most because...

I am a true Directioner because...

1D are...
Gorgeous
Talented
Funny
Focused
Handsome
Interesting
Amazing
Creative

Now when I look at One Direction:

I think...

Now I love _____ the most because...

I will always be a Directioner because...

35

The 1D Story

The Beginning

I ♥ 1D

Over the course of six months in 2010, Harry, Liam, Louis, Niall and Zayn went from being unknown teenage pop wannabes to singing sensations. Yep, we're talking about *The X Factor*...

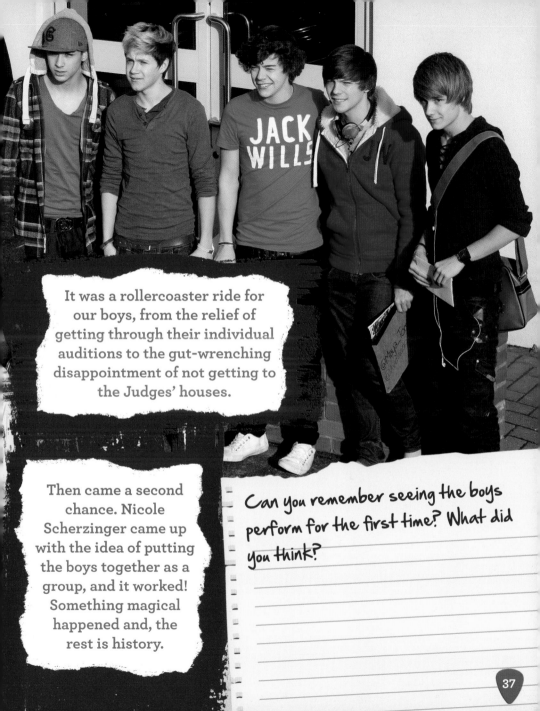

It was a rollercoaster ride for our boys, from the relief of getting through their individual auditions to the gut-wrenching disappointment of not getting to the Judges' houses.

Then came a second chance. Nicole Scherzinger came up with the idea of putting the boys together as a group, and it worked! Something magical happened and, the rest is history.

Can you remember seeing the boys perform for the first time? What did you think?

The Auditions

Totally terrifying, luckily our boys weren't scared off by *The X Factor* auditions.

Harry

Liam

Song: 'Isn't She Lovely' by Stevie Wonder
Location: Manchester

Judges:	Vote:
Louis	No
Nicole	Yes
Simon	Yes

Louis said Harry was 'not experienced or confident enough'.

Song: 'Cry Me a River' made famous by various artists including Ella Fitzgerald and Michael Bublé
Location: Birmingham

Judges:	Vote:
Simon	Yes
Louis	Yes
Cheryl	Yes
Natalie Imbruglia	Yes

Louis

Song: 'Hey There Delilah' by The Plain White T's
Location: Manchester

Judges:	Vote:
Louis	Yes
Nicole	Yes
Simon	Yes

Niall

Song: 'So Sick' by Ne-Yo
Location: Dublin

Judges:	Vote:
Louis	Yes
Cheryl	No
Simon	Yes
Katy Perry	Yes

Katy had the deciding vote.

Zayn

Song: 'Let Me Love You' by Mario
Location: Manchester

Judges:	Vote:
Louis	Yes
Nicole	Yes
Simon	Yes

My favourite audition was...

Mashup

Do you spend hours gazing at Harry's lush locks or Louis' chiselled jaw? We've created this cheeky quiz to test how well you know the 1D boys' faces close-up. Look closely and see if you can tell which facial features belong to whom!

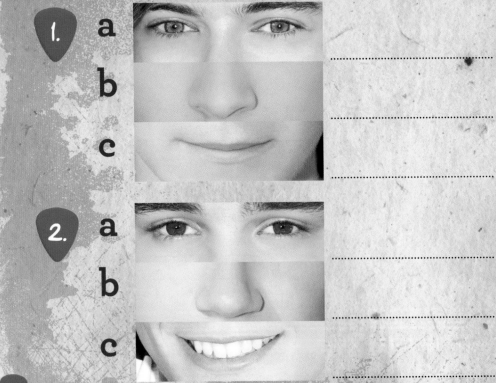

1.
a
b
c

....

....

....

2.
a

b

c

....

....

....

3.

a
b
c

....

....

....

4.

a
b
c

....

....

....

5.

a
b
c

....

....

....

Check answers on page 154

The 1D Story

The Shows

I ♥ 1D

Then it was into the knock-out rounds. Would the One Direction boys have time to gel? Could they share the stage? You bet they could...

One Direction didn't win *The X Factor* but they certainly won our hearts!

My favourite performance was...

on week...

42

Week 1:
Theme: *Number one singles*
Song: *'Viva la Vida' by Coldplay*
Result: *Safe*

Week 2:
Theme: *Heroes*
Song: *'My Life Would Suck Without You' by Kelly Clarkson*
Result: *Safe*

Week 3:
Theme: *Guilty pleasures*
Song: *'Nobody Knows' by Pink*
Result: *Safe*

Week 4:
Theme: *Halloween*
Song: *'Total Eclipse of the Heart' by Bonnie Tyler*
Result: *Safe*

Week 5:
Theme: *American anthems*
Song: *'Kids in America' by Kim Wilde*
Result: *Safe*

Week 6:
Theme: *Songs by Elton John*
Song: *'Something About the Way You Look Tonight'*
Result: *Safe*

Week 7:
Theme: *Songs by The Beatles*
Song: *'All You Need Is Love'*
Result: *Safe*

Week 8:
Theme: *Rock*
Songs: *'Summer of '69' by Bryan Adams and 'You Are So Beautiful' by Joe Cocker*
Result: *Safe*

Week 9:
Theme: *Club classics/ song to get to the final*
Song: *'Only Girl (In the World)' by Rhianna and 'Chasing Cars' by Snow Patrol*
Result: *Safe*

Week 10:

Final Show 1:
Themes: *Celebrity duets*
Songs: *'Your Song' by Elton John and 'She's the One' by Robbie Williams – performed with Robbie*
Result: *Safe*

Final Show 2:
Themes: *Winner's single*
Song: *'Torn' by Natalie Imbruglia*
Result: *Third*

43

Digits

Just in case you hadn't realised how fabulous **1D** truly are (as if!) we have put together some amazing facts and figures to prove it. Get ready to be blinded by numbers!

1 Guinness World Record (for being the first British group in US chart history to achieve a number one with their debut album)

2 BRIT Awards

3 Number one singles in the UK

4 Nights in Belfast on the 'Take Me Home' tour

5 Hot boys

6 Weeks at the top of the Irish album charts for 'Take Me Home'

7 Dates at London's O2 Arena in 2013

13 Delicious tracks on 'Take Me Home'

16 Sweet Harry's age when he auditioned for The X Factor

32 The number of countries where 'Take Me Home' went to number one

I ♥ HARRY

I ♥ LIAM

I ♥ LOUIS

I ♥ NIALL

I ♥ ZAYN

67
Cities visited on the 'Take Me Home' tour

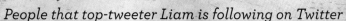

14,000+
People that top-tweeter Liam is following on Twitter

20,000
Directioners filled London's O2 Arena at each concert on the 'Take Me Home' tour

155,000
Copies of 'Take Me Home' sold in the UK in the first week of its release

53,000,000+
Fans following the boys' individual Twitter pages

12,000,000+
Followers for the official One Direction Twitter page

Sizzlin' Sudoku

This game of Sudoku will put your 1D wits to the test. Each column, row and 6 x 6 grid should contain all five boys and the band logo.

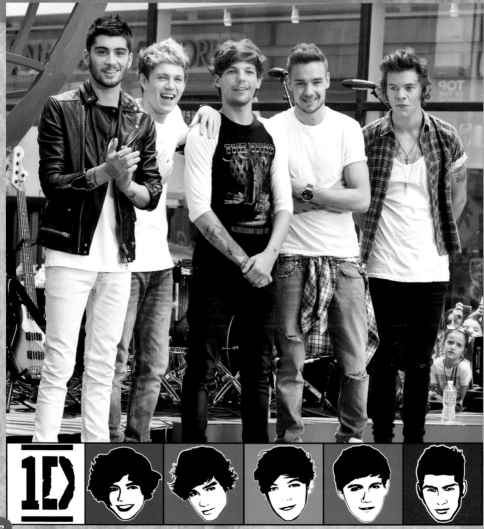

Either write in their names, colour in the correct boxes or if you have art smarts, why not draw the guys in!

Check answers on page 154

Drop-dead gorgeous 'Hazza' gives it his all, performing at the Brit Awards 2013.

48

I ♥ HARRY

Harry

49

Shadow Secrets

Are you a dedicated Directioner? Can you spot the boys from their shadows alone? Check out this pic - there are four shadows but only one of them matches it exactly.

Check answers on page 155

Can you spot the right one?

1.

2.

3.

4.

I ♥ HARRY.
LIAM.
LOUIS.
NIAll
ZAYN

My 1D Melody

1D's perfect voices turn musical poems into amazing songs. Have a go at writing your own song for the boys to sing - even if it's only in your head! Note down which One Direction member should sing each part.

Title: ....

My song is about: ....

My inspiration was: ....

Sung by:

Verse 1:

Chorus:

All!

Verse 2:

Verse 3:

Verse 4:

I ♥ ONE DIRECTION

Write about something really important to you.

The  Story

'Up All Night'

One Direction's debut album, 'Up All Night', went to number one in 17 countries! The album was recorded in Sweden, the UK and the US. It was released in Autumn 2011 and was the start of the boys conquering the world with their music.

The first single of, 'Up All Night' – 'What Makes You Beautiful', starts the album off with an up-tempo funky feel. We couldn't stop dancing!

Loads of cool writers and producers wanted to work with One Direction, right from the beginning. The lucky ones included writer, Rami Yacoub, (who has worked with everyone, from Britney to Bon Jovi), producers Steve Mac (Westlife, JLS), Red One (Lady Gaga, JLo), Carl Falk (Akon, Taio Cruz) and Toby Gad (Beyoncé, Alicia Keys, Fergie).

All the hard work was certainly worth it! The lads produced a debut album that stormed charts around the world and ensured fans for decades to come. It will go down in history as one of the most exciting and creative albums ever!

What Makes You Beautiful
Gotta Be You
One Thing
More Than This
Up All Night
I Wish
Tell Me A Lie
Taken
I Want
Everything About You
Same Mistakes
Save You Tonight
Stole My Heart

My favourite song from the 'Up All Night' album is

because...

55

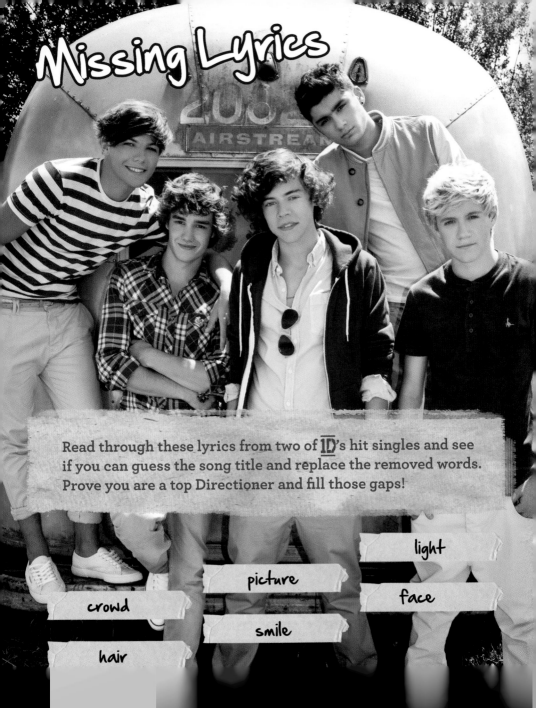

Missing Lyrics

Read through these lyrics from two of 1D's hit singles and see if you can guess the song title and replace the removed words. Prove you are a top Directioner and fill those gaps!

light

picture

face

crowd

smile

hair

Song Title: ....

Baby you ▭▭▭▭ up my world like nobody else,

The way that you flip your ▭▭▭▭ gets

me overwhelmed,

But when you ▭▭▭▭ at

the ground it ain't hard to tell,

You don't know...

Song Title: ....

Whenever I close my eyes,

I ▭▭▭▭ you there

I'm looking out at the ▭▭▭▭,

you're everywhere

I'm watching you from the stage yeah

You're smile is on every ▭▭▭▭ now...

Check answers on page 155

The 1D Story

'Take Me Home'

1D's second album, 'Take Me Home', was the most hotly anticipated new album of years. The guys had smashed it first time around with, 'Up All Night' and it was time to see if they could do it again! 'Take Me Home' was released in November 2012 and topped the charts in a staggering 37 countries!

The guys used many of the same writers and producers who had worked on their first album but got other go-to music giants involved aswell. They asked Dr. Luke, Katy Perry's top producer to work his magic and asked buddy, Ed Sheeran to pen some tracks too. The result is 42 amazing minutes of soft-rock ('Summer of Love'), dance-pop ('C'mon, C'mon') and emotional folk ('Little Things').

On it's realease the album hit the No1 spot on pre-order charts in 50 countries! It sold over a million copies worldwide in the first week in the UK and the US. One thing is for sure – this album is going to be on our music systems for years to come!

Live While We're Young
Kiss You
Little Things
C'mon, C'mon
Last First Kiss
Heart Attack
Rock Me
Change My Mind
I Would
Over Again
Back For You
They Don't Know About Us
Summer Love

My favourite song from the 'Take Me Home' album is

because...

59

Covered!

Artwork for albums and singles are designed to grab your attention, tell you how amazing the band is, and get you to buy their music! Get your creative hat on and give it a go...

What would you have designed for the cover of 'Take Me Home'.

Design the cover for ID's next album and give it a title! - Tough stuff.

If you were in a band, what would your album look like?

61

Perfect Playlist

My 1D Party Playlist

1	
2	
3	
4	
5	
6	
7	
8	
9	
10	

One Direction have given us a ton of amazing music. In fact there's so much it's time to get organised – use the tables to sketch out your perfect 1D playlists. Try making a fast-paced one for a party, and a chillaxed one, ideal for Sundays

My 1D Sunday Playlist	
1	
2	
3	
4	
5	
6	
7	
8	
9	
10	

Now compare your playlists to your friends'. Are they as in tune with the boys as you?

Band-agrams

Take a look at these jumbles of letters. Unscramble each one to reveal the name of a person who has been important to the guys in their journey as a band.

Use the clues if you get stuck...

1.

DAMOS NERJEC

Clue: *"I knew Louis from his early acting career."*

2.

EATR YKRPY

Clue: *"Niall kissed me, I think he liked it!"*

3.

LEMON WOCILS

Clue: *"I believed in the boys right from the start."*

4.

SE DEHENAR

Clue: "I wrote the song 'Little Things' for 1D."

5.

OSCNLG ZHEIRINEER

Clue: "I decided to put the guys together as a band."

The lovely Liam looking dapper on the red carpet – yummy!

I ♥ LIAM

67

Get Your Groove On

Can you spot ten differences between these two gorgeous pics?

68

The feisty five are doing what they do best and rockin' the stage!

Check answers on page 155

'Take Me Home' World Tour

The 'Take Me Home' world tour has been massive! 1D hit the road on 23rd February 2013 with dates in the UK and Europe and then they were off around the globe. It has been quite a ride...

Harry, Liam, Louis, Niall and Zayn played a mega six-day run of shows at London's O2 Arena. Tickets sold out in minutes and we're not talking hundreds; the O2 Arena's capacity is 20,000 people!

The boys set a dress code for their Dutch Directioners taking to the stage dressed all in orange which is the national colour of the Netherlands.

Some Norwegian Directioners were so excited to see gorgeous Harry outside his hotel, they pounced on him and he had to be rescued by security. We don't blame them!

1D played to 15,000 lucky Directioners in a 2000-year-old Roman amphitheatre.

The guys wowed the States, night after night for 41 dates. And finally ended the North American leg of the 'Take Me Home' world tour at The Staples Center, Los Angeles.

Harry tweeted, 'That's it. North American tour over, and I have been left speechless by your continued support. Without you, we don't exist.. so thank you.'

71

Globe Trotters

GREENLAND (DENMARK)

ICELAND

FAROE ISLANDS

NORWAY

CANADA

Vancouver, Canada

Seattle, USA

UNITED KINGDOM

IRELAND

GERMANY

London, UK

FRANCE

Toronto, Canada

UNITED STATES OF AMERICA

Los Angeles, USA

Washington D.C., USA

PORTUGAL

SPAIN

MOROCCO

ALGERIA

MEXICO

THE BAHAMAS

CUBA

MAURITANIA

MALI

NIGER

BURKINA FASO

GHANA

NIGERIA

COTE D'IVOIRE

CAPE VERDE

	Landmarks:	City:
1	Sydney Harbour Bridge	
2	Hollywood sign	
3	The White House	
4	One Tree Hill	
5	Tokyo Tower	
6	Capilano Suspension Bridge	
7	Big Ben	
8	The CN Tower	

Check answers on page 155

One Direction love to be on tour because it allows them to meet their amazing fans all over the world. They also manage a bit of cheeky sightseeing!

Check out the ID tour map and match the famous landmarks to the cities where they belong.

Tokyo, Japan

Sydney, Australia

Perth, Australia

Auckland, New Zealand

Christchurch, New Zealand

On Tour Word Puzzle

The 1D boys have proved themselves the hardest working band in pop by touring across the globe. Check out our tour inspired word puzzle and see if you can unscramble all fifteen words. Then use the letters that appear in boxes to unscramble the final message.

ONE DIRECTION
One Direction Presents

ONE DIRECTION
One Direction Presents
ONE DIRECTION
PLUS SPECIAL GUESTS
(VIP) FRONT ROW
Enter Via Door:2
56780753547

Enter Via Door:2
56780753547

^ A78

The words hidden are all tour related. For example, where 1D go on tour, where they stay, how they get there, what they do. Even what the Directioners get up to! Put your thinking caps on...

Hint - it's a treat for 2014!

Answer:

	W								

NAERA

PEOREU

CUSMI

TORU SUB

MARIECA

DULDEH

TELHO

SAAI

VEETIRWIN

FSGAL

SARAALUTIA

MEHO

FASN

KU

COWDR

Check answers on page 155

Amphitheatre Adventure

One Direction have a dream gig in the beautiful Italian city of Verona. They're due on stage in one hour, but they got lost on the way. Yikes!

Can you help them find the amphitheatre?

Start

Check answer on page 155

Finish

77

Tour X-posed

True ✓

✗ False

We get to hear about what Harry, Liam, Louis, Niall and Zayn are up to on tour via Twitter and in the entertainment news. Sometimes their experiences sound a bit too weird/wacky/funny/scary to be true. Time for you to decide whether the tour tales below are fact or fantasy.

1. The boys have included a cover version of 'Seven Nation Army' by The White Stripes in their live shows – super cool!

✓ ✗

2. The boys have been re-enacting The Inbetweeners dance on stage – just because!

✓ ✗

3. In Montreal, one Directioner was so keen to get a glimpse of Liam that she fell through a glass window – be careful out there!

✓ ✗

4. 1D found Norway to be pretty chilly, so took to the stage in their One Direction onesies – stylish!

✓ ✗

5.

Zayn and Louis had their own Scooby Doo inspired Mystery Machine van made so that they can tour America in style – how cool is that!

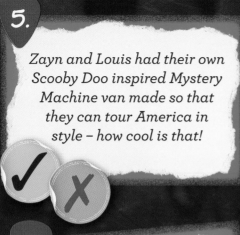

6.

Niall did the 'Mullingar shuffle' with an Irish flag hanging out of the back of his jeans at their Dublin show – looking good Nialler!

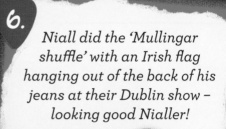

7.

For their Amsterdam show, the boys tweeted Directioners telling them to come to the gig wearing red – go Directioners!

8.

Louis dared Niall to roly-poly his way across the stage at their show in Hershey – awww!

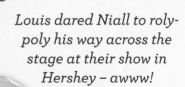

Vidz Quiz

The **1D** boys love making videos for their hit singles. It's obvious how much fun they have doing it. Use our video quiz as an excuse to watch them all again, and then test your memory with the questions below!

1. Which video features tents and a lot of bunting?

2. In which video do the boys busk on the streets of London?

3. In which video do the boys show off some fancy knitwear on the ski slope?

4. What colour is the **1D** campervan in the video for 'What Makes You Beautiful'?

Check answers on page 156

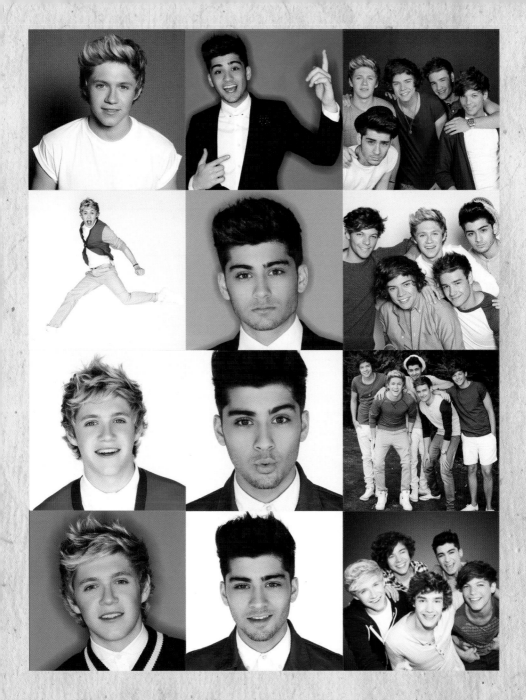

5. In which video does Zayn jump aboard a steam train?

6. In the video for 'Kiss You', which boy wears arm bands during the surfing scene?

7. Which video is shot in black and white and features the boys singing in the studio?

8. In the video for 'Live While We're Young' who jumps off a swing into the river?

9. Which video features space hoppers and a red London bus?

10. In which video are the boys running around on a beach?

Take a peek at this sizzlin' shot of Louis. We could lose hours staring into those eyes!

I ♥
LOUIS

Louis ¹⁵

The  Story

Style

Style has always been important to the One Direction boys.

They all love fashion and it's helped them create a strong, united image, as a band. They mix designer threads and high street favourites to form a slick and stylish stage look. Whether they are performing to thousands of fans, travelling around the globe or just hanging out they always know how to dress to impress!

Harry

Tailoring features heavily in Harry's signature style. He is rarely without jackets, blazers or a tux. Harry loves to put his own stamp on things with a quirky accessory or two. Favourites include bow-ties and pocket handkerchiefs. He's definitely one dapper chap!

Liam

Liam is arguably the most versatile of the group in terms of style. He looks equally comfortable in a suit or sweatpants. Liam loves shirts! Whether they're checked or polo, he's never out of these fashion classics.

Louis

Louis is a beanie enthusiast – he loves to accessorize every possible outfit with one. He certainly knows what works for him and mixes slim fit chinos with casual tees and crisp white shirts.

Niall

Niall is a big fan of informal! He mixes stylish casual separates to create a fresh sporty look. Hoodies and Hi-tops are a must for the man from Mullingar. And in terms of footwear, the brighter the better.

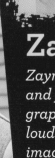

Zayn

Zayn loves to merge a rocker-street look and preppy style. He mixes biker jackets, graphic tees and tons of layering. His loud look certainly fits with his bad boy image. Accessories range from large stud earrings to a gorgeous blonde quiff.

85

Style SOS

We know that Harry, Liam, Louis, Niall and Zayn have amazing individual style but can you identify them by just their clothes? Time to test your knowledge of 1D fashion!

1.

2.

3.

4.

5.

Check answers on page 156

Top Tweets

Match the tweets to the right lad...

Harry

1. 'Can't believe we released a PERFUME today all because of a tweet we got from you lot! :) Big love'

2. 'What's everyone doing? I just woke up! Probs gonna go back asleep!'

3. 'Cant believe its the last show tonight. I have loved every single bit of America. Thank you sooo much to everyone who came. Best fans everrr'

4. 'Amazing show today !! Loved it ! Can't believe we just played the staples centre! Sickkkkkkkk'

5. 'Went to watch Cirque du Soleil tonight. I now feel very not bendy.'

6. 'Can't wait for you to see the movie, anybody thinking of going to see it?'

7. 'Soooo excited 19 days to my bday and 19 days till our movie is out in the UK!'

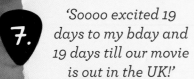

8. 'Wow 3 years today. Really is so hard to comprehend. What an amazing world all of you amazing people have created for us. Thank you.'

9. 'Wow! 13 million followers! U guys are amazing! Welcome to my world anyone who has just joined us here!! It can be quite random at times!'

10. 'Goodnight Vegas :) great show tonight x'

Check answers on page 156

'It's going to be fantastic. You really get to know the guys. So proud of them.'
Simon Cowell.

It feels as if we have been waiting for years and years, but the 1D movie is here! The word on the street is that director Morgan Spurlock's team have shot enough footage to make a whole series of movies. So the big challenge has been choosing what to put into the movie and what to leave out, not to mention all the home movie action that the boys have shot themselves. While racing across the globe on the 'Take Me Home' tour, Harry, Liam, Louis, Niall and Zayn have been filming each other to give a real insight into their life on the road.

THIS IS US

1D3D

What do you want to know?

We were promised dazzling performances, down-to-earth footage and access to those behind-the-scenes moments – they didn't fail to deliver. And in 3D! The man in charge, Morgan Spurlock, has described the boys as 'free spirits', 'wild' and 'hilarious', and said what he loves most about 1D is how much they support each other. Ahhhh.

So you've seen the movie, just imagine you're a reporter with the chance to ask the boys anything about their mega movie.

What would your questions be?

Q1.

Q2.

Q3.

Q4.

THIS IS US

Quiz

Phew, so the movie is here. How many times have you seen it so far? Have you become an expert on all things This Is Us? Time to test yourself.

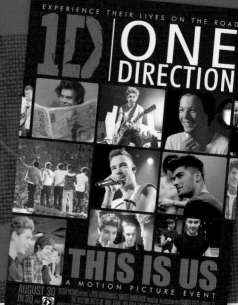

One Direction with Director Morgan Spurlock

The Questions...

1.

The poster for the movie features a mosaic of tiny:
a. pictures of Directioners ☐
b. pictures of One Direction ☐
c. pictures of the cities visited on tour ☐

2.

Name the five leading men in the movie.

....

....

....

....

....

3.

Has the movie been shot in
a. 2D film ☐
b. 3D film ☐
c. black and white ☐

4.

What was the UK release date?

....

5.

What is the name of the director of This Is Us?

....

....

6.

Which 1D member buys his mum a house, which features in the trailer?

....

7.

To show us what happens behind the scenes on tour, the boys:
a. were filmed by hidden cameras ☐
b. were given cameras so that they could film each other ☐
c. were asked to fill out questionnaires ☐

Super-cute Niall
shows off his Irish
charm and boyish
good looks.
Grrrrr!

I ♥ NIALL

Niall

Movie Montage

EXPERIENCE THEIR LIVES ON THE ROAD

1D | ONE DIRECTION

THIS IS US

A MOTION PICTURE EVEN

TRISTAR PICTURES PRESENTS A SYCO ENTERTAINMENT/MODEST! MANAGEMENT PRODUCTION IN ASSOCIATION WITH WARRIOR POETS/FULWE
ONE DIRECTION THIS IS US NIALL HORAN ZAYN MALIK LIAM PAYNE HARRY STYLES LOUIS TOMLINSON PIERRE
PRODUCTION TOM KRUEGER JOSEPH RICHARD GRIFFITH HARRY MAGEE WILL BLOOMFIELD DOUG MERRIFIELD JEREMY CHILNICK MATTHEW
PRODUCED SIMON COWELL ADAM MILANO MORGAN SPURLOCK BEN WINSTON MORGAN S
DIRECTED MORGAN S

AUGUST 30
IN 3D AND
real D 3D
TO GET YOUR TICKETS FIRST
FOLLOW @1DThisIsUs

SONY
Modest!

THIS FILM IS NOT YET RATED
FOR FUTURE INFO GO TO FILMRATING.COM

How cool is the official movie poster for *This is Us*? The background is made up of lots of tiny photos of Directioners that were submitted by fans everywhere. Are you in there?

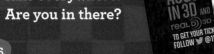

Make your own mosaic of Directioners that you know and love in the box below. Draw yourself and your friends, but only the ones that are as crazy about 1D as you are.

The 1D Story

1D have been riding high in 2013 and the world knows it!

Awards '13

If you were able to give 1D a prize for something in 2013, what would it be? Top Group? Hotties of the Year? Favourite Song? Below are just some of the awards that our talented and hard-working boys have received this year:

BRIT Awards

Global Success

Wow! Wake up and find out that we've won 3 billboard awards! Can't believe it! Thank you so much best fans ever! Love you soo much. xxxxxxx' Tweet by Niall

Billboard Music Awards

Top New Artist
Top Duo/Group
Top Pop Artist

Nickelodeon Kids' Choice Awards US

Favourite Song:
'What Makes You Beautiful'

Nickelodeon Kids' Choice Awards UK

Favourite UK Band

People's Choice Awards

Favourite Album: 'Up All Night'
Favourite Song:
'What Makes You Beautiful'

Radio Disney Music Awards

Best Music Group

Teen Choice Awards

Choice Summer Tour
Choice Group
Choice Single: 'Live While We're Young'
Choice Love Song: 'Little Things'

And there will be more to come!

Keep following all **1D** news and fill in the results of the awards as they're announced.

Award:

Category:

Result:

Award:

Category:

Result:

Award:

Category:

Result:

Award:

Category:

Result:

And guess what?

You won an award too:
Radio Disney Music Awards

Fiercest Fans

99

Cryptic Chords Wordsearch

Take a look at the clues below. Can you guess the single or album titles? Most of the clues are lyrics from the song, so start humming those tunes. Once you've figured it out write them in the space, then find them in the wordsearch grid. They may be written forwards, backwards, up, down or diagonally.

1. **1D**'s first album

2. 'So get out, get out, get out of my head'

3. 'Can we fall one more time?/ Stop the tape and rewind'

4. 'When he opens his arms and holds you close tonight/It just won't feel right'

5. **1D**'s second album

6. 'Oh, tell me, tell me, tell me how to turn your love on'

7. 'Your hand fits in mine/Like it's made just for me'

8. Not a single but a bonus track: 'You know I'll be/ Your life/Your voice/ Your reason to be'

Don't add spaces between words when searching for titles in the grid!

R	W	O	X	S	T	H	G	I	N	L	L	A	P	U
L	O	T	F	B	A	U	M	G	I	Q	P	N	A	P
I	V	U	H	W	K	I	S	S	Y	O	U	J	C	S
T	E	T	O	B	E	C	O	D	X	A	Y	P	O	E
T	R	E	F	Y	M	O	S	T	R	X	D	V	N	W
L	H	T	Q	I	E	P	Y	O	S	U	J	K	E	T
E	D	O	R	U	H	B	T	N	F	S	P	I	T	Y
T	E	M	P	E	O	R	A	W	Z	I	U	S	H	O
H	P	B	U	S	M	G	A	T	H	Y	D	W	I	P
I	R	S	T	N	E	M	O	M	T	E	G	V	N	U
N	T	D	A	F	C	O	G	S	T	O	M	I	G	D
G	U	M	Y	O	H	Y	P	I	A	F	G	B	E	S
S	C	U	P	T	R	F	A	D	Q	O	T	X	E	K
R	U	B	T	A	I	C	P	U	S	Z	E	E	D	P
E	S	I	H	T	N	A	H	T	E	R	O	M	X	O

Check answers on page 156

Star Story

What do our star signs say about us? For hundreds of years people have believed that our date of birth tells us something about our personality. Let's test the theory and look at Harry, Liam, Louis, Niall and Zayn's star signs in detail.

Aries 21 March – 19 April	**Taurus** 20 April – 20 May	**Gemini** 21 May – 20 June
Cancer 21 June – 22 July	**Leo** 23 July – 22 August	**Virgo** 23 August – 22 September
Libra 23 September – 22 October	**Scorpio** 23 October – 21 November	**Sagittarius** 22 November – 21 December
Capricorn 22 December – 19 January	**Aquarius** 20 January – 18 February	**Pisces** 19 February – 20 March

Virgo

Both Niall and Liam share the sign Virgo.

Virgo personality: *Modest, shy, hard-working, kind-hearted, caring, creative, sensitive*

How would you describe Niall?...

How would you describe Liam?...

Virgos are a good match for: *Capricorn, Cancer and Taurus*

Is Niall a typical Virgo?   Y/N

Is Liam a typical Virgo?   Y/N

Capricorn

Zayn and Louis are both Capricorns.

Capricorn personality: *Humorous, sensible, practical, hard-working, sensitive, loyal*

How would you describe Zayn?...

How would you describe Louis?...

Capricorns are a good match for: *Taurus, Virgo and Leo*

Is Zayn a typical Capricorn?   Y/N

Is Louis a typical Capricorn?   Y/N

Aquarius:

Harry is an Aquarius.

Aquarius personality: *Original, friendly, charming, caring, thoughtful*

How would you describe Harry?...

Aquarians are a good match for: *Gemini, Libra and Virgo*

Is Harry a typical Aquarius?   Y/N

Your Star Story

Now it's your turn. Do a little research and enter your details.

My star sign is:
_____
_____

The characteristics of a ....
are:
_____
_____
_____
_____
_____

I would describe myself as:
_____
_____
_____
_____
_____
_____

I am a typical .... True/False

Now write your dream horoscope involving the **1D** boys. Have a recap of the zodiac profiles on the previous page. Who are you most compatible with? Is this who you've always imagined yourself with? Or does your star story take an unexpected twist...

What...

When...

Who...

Make your predictions – maybe they'll come true!

Miami Mayhem

Help! It is one hour before One Direction are due on stage in Miami for a sell-out show, but they are one band member short. Liam set off to do a spot of surfing hours ago but he isn't back yet.

Start

Can you guide him through the streets of Miami and reunite him with his band mates?

Check answer on page 156

Finish

Choice Tunes

Our taste in music tells people a lot about us. What will Harry, Liam, Louis, Niall and Zayn's fave songs tell you about them?

Draw a line between the boy and the two tracks you think are his favourites.

Check answers on page 156

1. *'Thriller' by Michael Jackson*

2. *'All Back' by Chris Brown*

3. *'Shine on You Crazy Diamond' by Pink Floyd*

4. *'Viva La Vida' by Coldplay*

5. *'Crazy Love' by Michael Bublé*

6. *'Look After You' by The Fray*

7. *'Wake Me Up' by Ed Sheeran*

 8.

'Lady in Red' by Chris de Burgh

9.

'Angels' by Robbie Williams

10.

'Suit and Tie' by Justin
Timberlake ft. Jay Z

You may not have
heard of them
all – if not check
them out!

My favourite songs are:

Sound Check

Can you recognise the boys from just their voices? Read the lyrics below, hits played on 1D's awesome albums and see if you can work out who sang what.

1.

'Up All Night'

*'Katy Perry's on replay
She's on replay
DJ got the floor to shake,
    the floor to shake
People going all the way
Yeah, all the way
I'm still wide awake'*

The singer is:

I ♥ HARRY

2.

'Live While We're Young'

*'Yeah, we'll be doing what we do
Just pretending that we're cool and we
    know it too (know it too)
Yeah, we'll keep doing what we do
Just pretending that we're cool, so tonight'*

The singer is:

I ♥ LIAM

Check answers on page 157

3. 'Little Things'

'And I've just let these little
   things slip out of my mouth
'Cause it's you,
Oh, it's you,
It's you they add up to
And I'm in love with you
And all these little things'

The singer is:

4. 'Kiss You'

'Oh, I just wanna show you
   off to all of my friends
Making them drool down their
   chinny-chin-chins
Baby, be mine tonight,
   mine tonight
Baby, be mine tonight, yeah'

The singer is:

5. 'One Thing'

'I've tried playing it cool
But when I'm looking at you
I can't ever be brave
'Cause you make my
   heart race'

The singer is:

111

Wordsmith

One Direction's, 'Where We Are' stadium tour is going to be the biggest thing in 2014! The excitement is growing and we can't wait. Join the excitement and see how many words you can make from the phrase, 'One Big Announcement'. We have started you off with a couple of examples.

I ♥ ONE DIRECTION

'One Big Announcement'

1. meat
2. once
3.
4.
5.
6.
7.
8.
9.
10.

11.
12.
13.
14.
15.
16.
17.
18.
19.
20.

Rewind

2012 seems such a long time ago. Can you cast your mind back and remember all the cool things that One Direction were up to? It was a massive year for them and they have been riding high ever since!

1. At which sporting event's closing ceremony did **1D** perform in 2012?

2. In which country did One Direction break records for being the first UK band to see their first two albums debut at the top of the chart?

3. What awards did **1D** win at the Nickelodeon Kids' Choice Awards in 2012?

4. In 2012, 1D won best British Single at the BRIT awards for which song?

5. Which song did 1D perform at *The X Factor* final in 2012?

6. Can you name all 1D's singles from 2012?

7. What did 1D host a global viewing party for on Twitter in May 2012?

8. Who injured his knee and ended up on crutches?

9. Who celebrated their 21st birthday on Christmas Eve?

10. 1D attended the US premiere of which movie, armed with nerf guns?

Check answers on page 157

We ♥ ONE DIRECTION

We know how hard it is to choose your favourite 1D crush. So we've tried to make it easier for you! Work your way through the questions below and enter the name of your favourite 1D member for each category. Then see who comes out on top!

Looks

- Who has the most beautiful eyes?
- Who has the coolest hair?
- Who has the loveliest smile?
- Who is the most stylish?

And the winner for looks is:

Personality

- Who is the cutest?
- Who is the most charming?

- Who is the most funny?

- Who is the kindest?
- Why?

And the winner for personality is:

Performer

- Who has the best voice?
- Who has the best moves?
- Who knows how to work the camera?

And the winner for performance is:

My favourite is

I ♥ HARRY
LIAM
LOUIS
NIAll
ZAYN

I decided he was my favourite because:

If I had to describe him in three words, they would be:

If I could spend just one day with him:

We would spend the morning...

I would wear:

He would wear:

We would spend the afternoon...

If I bought him a present, it would be:

In the evening we would...

Because...

I would want to tell him:

I would remember it forever

because...

117

Picture Perfect

OMG! This jaw-dropping snap of the lads is incomplete.

Take a close look at the puzzle pieces on the opposite page. Which fit the bill and complete the picture?

1.

2.

3.

4.

5.

6.

A. B. C.

D. E. F.

G. H. I.

J. K. L.

Check out this heart-melting picture of Zayn. How much would we ♥ to share a day in the sun with him?

I ♥ ZAYN

121

The 1D Story

Famous Directioners

We know that 1D are loved by Directioners across the world, but it is super-cool when celebs start biggin' up the boys. Check out the selection of tweets below and feel the love.

One Big Announcement

Ash from 1D's support band, 5 Seconds of Summer:

'So proud of our bro's @onedirection <3 that is just crazy and epically inspiring, one day boys ONE DAY!! :D -ash xx'

Aston from JLS:

'Huge congrats to... all the 1D boys on their tour announcement HUGE stuff!!'

Fantasy Football

Real Madrid legend, Sergio Ramos shares the pitch with 1D:

'Today I met @OneDirection guys. A great picture with them. Greetings!!'

Rio Ferdinand on the 1D concert experience:

'Just at the 1Direction concert... eardrums are struggling... never heard so much screaming!! Aaaaaaaaaahhhhhhh!!! Lads on fire!'

Proud Judges

Katy Perry gave Niall a 'yes' for his audition when she was a guest judge on *The X Factor*. She clearly made the right decision:

'Congratulations, you didn't let me down.'

Simon Cowell:

'One Direction continue to amaze me. Hard workers but still the nicest guys you could hope to work with.'

Best Buddies

Justin Bieber on hanging out with his new mates:

'Chillin' with the homies.'

And showing his respect:

'Congrats to my dudes @onedirection for the #1 album on iTunes.'

Olly Murs on comparing chest hair with Niall:

'Mr Horan @NiallOfficial loving the new chest hair dude... #niallsgrowingaloverug'

Me + My BFF

Now you've had the lowdown on 1D and their besties, it's time to think about you and yours! It is often easier to see the things we love and admire in other people. It's time to think about yourself and your friends in the same way.

My name is...

My nicknames are:

My eyes are:

My hair colour is:

My home town is:

My star sign is:

My top talents are:

I am best known for being:

My style could be described as:

My BFF loves me because:

Photo

Signed:

My BFF is...

Their nicknames are:

Their eyes are:

Their hair colour is:

Their home town is:

Their star sign is:

Their top talents are:

They are best known for being:

Their style could be described as:

They are my BFF because:

Photo

Signed:

If you get stuck, sit down with your BFF and ask for some inspiration. And don't forget to share your thoughts with them about why they are the best!

125

Dreaming

Date:

Dear Diary,

The thing I love most about **1D** is...

If I met the band we would go to...

I would take...

I would wear...

We would talk about...

Access All Areas

1.

2.

3.

4.

5.

6.

Time to see if you've really been keeping up! To the left are six snaps of **1D** on the red carpet or performing at various award ceremonies and shows around the globe. Once you've figured them out, write the name of the ceremony or show, into the correct space of the puzzle.

Don't add spaces between words when entering the names

Check answers on page 157

129

Best Bits

You adore the guys – that's obvious.
But what do you love most about them?
Which cute habits and quirky
sayings drive you wild?

Write
your **1D**
ultimate
best bits...

The band:

I loved it when...

It was so funny when...

It was so cute when...

You can tell they really care when...

I wish I'd been there when...

The music:

My favourite album is...

My favourite song is ...

My favourite line is...

I love it when .... *sings...*

Fashion:

The thing I love most about the band's style is...

I love it when they wear...

I love .... 's individual style because...

My best **1D** inspired outfit is...

True Love:

All I can think about is . . .

My secret crush is . . .

I am a true Directioner because...

Fantasy Gig

Harry, Liam, Louis, Niall and Zayn certainly know how to put on a show. As tickets for their third headline tour start to fly out, we're asking, if you were in charge, what would you do?

Use the spaces below to design your fantasy 1D gig!

Basics:

When –

Where –

Ticket Price –

Advertising:

Ticket design

Poster design

Theme:

Set design –

....

Props –

....

Costumes –

....

The Show:

Support act –

....

....

Set list –

....

....

....

....

....

....

....

....

....

After the show:

Backstage party guest list –

....

....

Drinks –

....

Food –

....

FIZ

Write an online review of your gig:

133

Ideal Crib

Wowza! The unbelievable has happened – One Direction are buying a house and they want you to design, decorate and make it **1D** perfect. Do a great job and you'll become their hottest houseguest.

Is that a rollercoaster!?

What's in the garage?

Crib List – 1D manor must-haves:

1. ....

2. ....

3. ....

4. ....

5. ....

Part One

Just for you, we have collected a whole load of need-to-know facts about One Direction - enjoy!

1. As part of Deaf Awareness Week 2013, a number of 1D songs were translated into sign language so that Directioners who are deaf can enjoy them too.

2. Louis and Zayn have had a van refurbished to look exactly like the Mystery Machine in Scooby Doo – looks like they will be touring in style!

3. Niall was scared of clowns when he was little. Awww!

4. Mega-star Johnny Depp once invited the boys to his Los Angeles pad for a jammin' session.

5. Louis once owned a car called Cheryl.

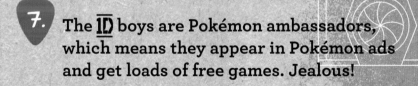

6. Dashing Harry suited up to be best man at his mum, Anne's wedding. We just wish we could have heard his speech!

7. The **1D** boys are Pokémon ambassadors, which means they appear in Pokémon ads and get loads of free games. Jealous!

8. Harry once claimed that if he were a girl he would probably have a crush on Zayn!

I ♥ HARRY

I ♥ LIAM

I ♥ LOUIS

I ♥ NIALL

I ♥ ZAYN

Part Two

1. Zayn's favourite vegetable is an avocado. Mmm, tasty!

2. Just like the real thing, One Direction's Madame Tussauds waxwork doubles have gone on tour! Among other places they will be hitting New York and Sydney.

3. Ever wondered which band member has the best moves? Well, according to *The X Factor* choreographer, Brian Friedman, it's Harry!

4. While on tour in Auckland, daring duo Liam and Louis bungee jumped 328 metres off a building. Brave boys!

5. The boys have faced a surprising problem on their 'Take Me Home' tour. They have had to step up security because their underwear keeps being stolen!

6. Rumour has it that Zayn is the most forgetful member of the band on tour, and has even been known to leave his passport behind. Whoops!

7. At 1D World in New York, you can buy life-size cardboard cut-outs of the boys. Apparently Harry and Niall sell the most.

8. Liam once dressed up as Batman for Halloween. Wish we'd seen that!

9. The USA's First Lady, Michelle Obama, once asked the boys to play a special gig for her daughters.

10. Some US Directioners were so desperate to meet the boys they hid in some stinky bins by the entrance to a venue and stayed there for four hours. Yuk!

I ♥ HARRY

I ♥ LIAM

I ♥ LOUIS

I ♥ NIALL

I ♥ ZAYN

rock-it at the Brits!

Here are the boys
displaying some model
behaviour in New York...
No wait, those are waxwork
figures of our scrumptious
lads. Sightseeing just got
a lot more interesting!

147

Code Cracker

The boys have written all their dedicated Directioners a secret note. Can you crack the code and read the message? Once you've discovered the secret, write the **1D** lads a coded reply...

8.5.25 4.9.18.5.3.20.9.15.14.5.18.19,

....

23.5.'4 12.9.11.5 · 20.15 19.1.25

....

20.8.1.14.11 25.15.21 6.15.18

....

1.12.12 27.15.21.18 1.13.1.26.9.14.7

....

19.21.16.16.15.18.20. 23.5 3.1.14.'20

....

23.1.9.20 20.15 19.5.5 25.15.21

....

1.12.12 15.14 15.21.18

....

'23.8.5.18.5 23.5 1.18.5' 19.20.1.4.9.21.13

....

20.15.21.18, 14.5.24.20 25.5.1.18!

....

142

Check answer on page 157

Now write a reply using the secret code!

'Where We Are, Our Band, Our Story'

One Direction have promised us a gorgeous glossy book for Christmas.

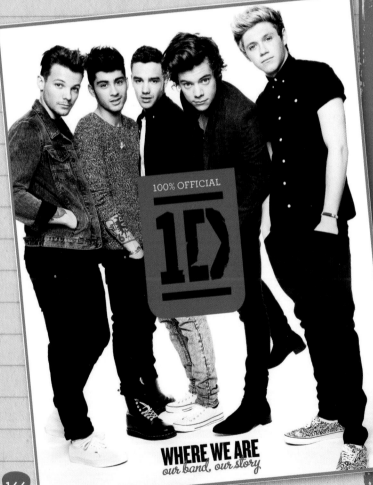

100% OFFICIAL

WHERE WE ARE
our band, our story

'Where We Are, Our Band, Our Story' will chart the amazing 1D story. From places they've visited and fans they've met, to their thoughts and feelings, highs and lows, hopes and dreams. We can't wait!

Put your design hat on and use the space to create your own book cover.

It needs to be eye-catching and to give
Directioners clues about what's inside.

Direction Perfection

You've designed the cover - now it's time to write your perfect 1D story. Fact or fiction, romance or fantasy. It's totally up to you. If you get stuck, flick back through this book for inspiration.

The beginning...

Ultimate Directioner Challenge

Now it's time recap and challenge yourself. This quiz will test your knowledge on all things **1D**, and determine if you are the ultimate Directioner!

Part One

1. Where did **1D** play a sold-out show in an amphitheatre on the 'Take Me Home' tour?

2. Which stadium will **1D** be playing in Dublin for two dates on the 'Where We Are' tour?

3. What is the name of **1D**'s fragrance?

4. What was the UK release date of the *This Is Us* movie?

5. What is the name of the director of **1D**'s movie?

6. Which guest judge on *The X Factor* tweeted Niall, 'Congratulations, you didn't let me down'?

7. How many BRIT awards have the boys won in total?

8. Which show did 1D ask Directioners to wear orange for?

9. Which two boys share the star sign Virgo?

10. How many Billboard awards did 1D win in 2013?

Check answers on page 157

Ultimate Directioner Challenge

Part Two

I ♥ ONE DIRECTION

11. Which *X Factor* Judge gave Harry a 'no' at his audition?

12. What is Zayn's star sign?

13. Where were the boys when they announced their 'Where We Are' tour?

14. Which two Canadian cities did **1D** play on the 'Take Me Home' tour?

15.

What was the name of **1D**'s Comic Relief single?

16. What was the first venue of the 'Take Me Home' tour?

17. How many countries will 1D perform in on the 'Take Me Home' tour in 2013?

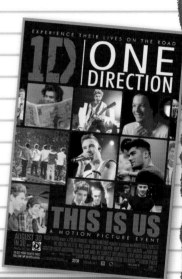

18. What is the name of the 1D single which features in their movie, *This Is Us*?

19. How many dates did 1D play at London's O2 Arena in 2013 on the 'Take Me Home' tour?

20. How many days, together as a band, did 1D celebrate in April 2013?

Check answers on page 157

I ♥ ONE DIRECTION

One final treat from the **1D** boys! Looking cool and collected on the red carpet of the Teen Choice Awards in California.

Answers

Page 12-13: Harry Mini-Quiz

1. – *b*, 2. – *c*, 3. – *c*, 4. – *a*, 5. – *b*

Page 16-17: Liam Wordsearch

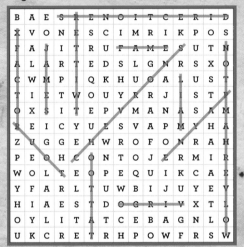

Page 20-21: Louis Spot the Difference

Page 24-25: Niall Crossword

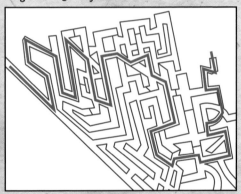

Page 28-29: Zayn Maze

Page 40-41: Mashup

1.	a) Harry	b) Zayn	c) Niall
2.	a) Liam	b) Naill	c) Louis
3.	a) Louis	b) Zayn	c) Liam
4.	a) Niall	b) Harry	c) Zayn
5.	a) Zayn	b) Louis	c) Harry

Page 46-47: Sizzlin' Sudoku

Logo = white
Harry = blue
Liam = green
Louis = orange
Niall = red
Zayn = purple

Page 50-51: Shadow Secrets

The correct shadow is number 2

Page 56-57: Missing Lyrics

Song Title: 'What Makes You Beautiful'
Baby you *light* up my world like nobody else,
The way that you flip your *hair* gets
    me overwhelmed,
But when you *smile* at the ground it ain't hard to tell,
You don't know'

Song Title: 'Back for you'
Whenever I close my eyes, I *picture* you there
I'm looking out at the *crowd*, you're everywhere
I'm watching you from the stage yeah
You're smile is on every *face* now

Page 64-65: Band-agrams

1. JAMES CORDEN
2. KATY PERRY
3. SIMON COWELL
4. ED SHEERAN
5. NICOLE SHERZINGER

Page 68-69: Get Your Groove On

Page 72-73: Globe Trotters

1. Sydney Harbour Bridge – Sydney, Australia
2. Hollywood sign – Los Angeles, USA
3. The White House – Washington D.C., USA
4. One Tree Hill – Auckland, New Zealand
5. Tokyo Tower – Tokyo, Japan
6. Capilano Suspension Bridge,
   – Vancouver, Canada
7. Big Ben – London, UK
8. The CN Tower – Toronto, Canada

Page 74-75: On Tour Word Puzzle

Clue	Answer
NAERA	ARENA
PEOREU	EUROPE
CUSMI	MUSIC
TORU SUB	TOUR BUS
MARIECA	AMERICA
DULDEH	HUDDLE
TELHO	HOTEL
SAAI	ASIA
VEETIRWIN	INTERVIEW
FSGAL	FLAGS
SARAALUTIA	AUSTRALASIA
MEHO	HOME
FASN	FANS
KU	UK
COWDR	CROWD

Answer: WHERE WE ARE WORLD TOUR

Page 76-77: Amphitheatre Adventure

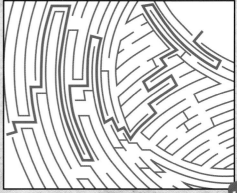

155

Answers

Page 78-79: Tour X-posed

1. *False*
2. *True*
3. *True*
4. *False*
5. *True*
6. *True*
7. *False*
8. *True*

Page 80-81: Vidz Quiz

1. *'Live While We're Young'*
2. *'One Thing'*
3. *'Kiss You'*
4. *Orange*
5. *'Gotta Be You'*
6. *Zayn*
7. *'Little Things'*
8. *Louis*
9. *'One Thing'*
10. *'What Makes You Beautiful'*

Page 86-87: Style SOS

1. *Louis*
2. *Zayn*
3. *Niall*
4. *Liam*
5. *Harry*

Page 88-89: Top Tweets

1. *Zayn*
2. *Niall*
3. *Liam*
4. *Louis*
5. *Harry*
6. *Harry*
7. *Liam*
8. *Louis*
9. *Niall*
10. *Zayn*

Page 92-93: This Is Us Quiz

1. *a*
2. *Easy! Harry Styles, Liam Payne, Louis Tomlinson, Niall Horan and Zayn Malik*
3. *b*
4. *29th August 2013*
5. *Morgan Spurlock*
6. *Zayn*
7. *b*

Page 100-101: Cryptic Chords Wordsearch

1. UP ALL NIGHT
2. ONE THING
3. GOTTA BE YOU
4. MORE THAN THIS
5. TAKE ME HOME
6. KISS YOU
7. LITTLE THINGS
8. MOMENTS

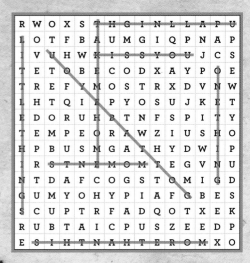

Page 106-107: Miami Mayhem

Page 108-109: Choice Tunes

Harry *'Lady in Red' by Chris de Burgh*
'Shine on You Crazy Diamond' by Pink Floyd

Liam *'Wake Me Up' by Ed Sheeran*
'Suit and Tie' by Justin Timberlake ft. Jay Z

Louis *'Look After You' by The Fray*
'Angels' by Robbie Williams

Niall *'Viva La Vida' by Coldplay*
'Crazy Love' by Michael Bublé

Zayn *'Thriller' by Michael Jackson*
'All Back' by Chris Brown

Page 110-111: Sound Check

The singer is:
1. *Harry*   2. *Zayn*   3. *Harry*
4. *Niall*   5. *Liam*

Page 114-115: Rewind

1. *London 2012 Olympics*
2. *USA*
3. *Favourite UK Band & Favourite UK Newcomer*
4. *'What Makes You Beautiful'*
5. *'Kiss You'*
6. *'One Thing' 'More Than This' 'Live While We're Young' 'Little Things'*
7. *The release of their DVD, 'Up All Night: The Live Tour'*
8. *Niall*
9. *Louis*
10. *Men in Black 3*

Page 118-119: Picture Perfect

1. *– c,* **2.** *– l,* **3.** *– g,* **4.** *– j,* **5.** *– e,* **6.** *– b*

Page 128-129: Access All Areas

1. *TEEN CHOICE AWARDS*
2. *NRJ MUSIC AWARDS*
3. *MTV EMAS*
4. *THE TODAY SHOW*
5. *BAMBI AWARDS*
6. *BRIT AWARDS*

Page 142-143: Code Cracker

Hey Directioners, we'd like to say thank you for all your amazing support. We can't wait to see you all on our 'Where We Are' stadium tour, next year!

Page 148-149: Ultimate Directioner Challenge – Part One

1. *Verona, Italy*
2. *Croke Park*
3. *'Our Moment'*
4. *29th August 2013*
5. *Morgan Spurlock*
6. *Katy Perry*
7. *Two*
8. *Amsterdam, The Netherlands*
9. *Niall and Liam*
10. *Three*

Page 150-151: Ultimate Directioner Challenge – Part Two

11. *Louis Walsh*
12. *Capricorn*
13. *Wembley Stadium, London*
14. *Toronto and Vancouver*
15. *'One Way or Another (Teenage Kicks)'*
16. *O2 Arena, London*
17. *21*
18. *'Best Song Ever'*
19. *Seven*
20. *1000*

I ♥ ONE DIRECTION

HARRY

LIAM